BRONCO BUSTER

by Dusty Chapman   illustrated by K. Bowser

Chapters

Harcourt

Orlando   Boston   Dallas   Chicago   San Diego

Visit *The Learning Site!*

www.harcourtschool.com

Leaving Home

My dad had a craggy face. I first noticed it on the day he turned me out. It was March 24, 1886—my fourteenth birthday.

"You're grown up, Billy Harder," he said. "Your mom and I figure it's time for you to move on. You've learned all you can on our little ranch."

I was glad to hear his words. For a time, I'd been feeling as corralled as the horses. I was eager to ride west and make a life of my own.

The next morning I kissed my mom good-bye and took off. Her tear-stained face was a little craggy, too. Ranch life was rough on her and Dad.

Within a week I had my first real job. I was riding herd on some longhorns being moved north to the railroad at Wichita, Kansas. At Wichita, they would be loaded onto trains and shipped to cities in the East.

All of a sudden, I had to dress like a cowhand. It took all the money I had saved to buy everything I needed. I got a big ten-gallon hat to keep the rain and sun off my head. I bought a big kerchief and learned how to tie it around my face. The kerchief would keep the dust out of my mouth.

I also bought leather chaps to protect my legs from bugs and brush along the trail. My dad had made sure I had the right boots. They had high heels so my feet wouldn't slip out of the stirrups.

On my new job, I did some of the things that a cowhand does. I kept the cattle together and made sure they didn't get mixed up with any other herds. At night, I helped find the cattle a good place to graze. Fortunately, I didn't have to protect them from rustlers. The cattle were already branded, so I didn't have to worry about that either.

There were always a few cows that wandered off. We couldn't allow any diversion from the trail, so I had to round them up. Sometimes I needed help with the ornery ones.

That was how Ty Webber and I became friends. He was twenty-two and had been a full-fledged cowhand for six years. Ornery cows were

no match for Ty. No matter how wild they were, the cows soon became compliant for him.

Ty had been turned out when he was thirteen, and he always missed his little brother. I suppose that's why he took a liking to me.

After a while Ty taught me how to deal with the ornery cows instead of doing the job himself. He taught me other things, too—things he'd learned on cattle drives all over Texas.

With lessons from Ty and my new hat and chaps, I figured I might be able to pass for a cowhand by the time we reached Wichita. Unfortunately, Ty's lessons came with a warning. He said that cowhands were a dying breed. Farms with fences spelled the end of cattle drives.

Moving On

Wichita, Kansas, was the biggest town I'd ever seen. I stayed there for about a month. By that time my money was running low, but luck was with me. I managed to sign on for another cattle drive in the spring. This time I was going to get cowhand wages. I was proud of myself. So I sent off a letter to Dad and Mom before riding back to Texas.

On the way I decided to trade my horse. I loved her, but Ty had warned me that she wasn't right for cowboy work. I didn't want to overwork her, but I wasn't about to trade her until I was sure she'd have a good home.

One day, just after I reached the Texas border, I stayed at a small ranch. At breakfast I mentioned wanting to trade my horse.

The rancher was interested. He wanted a compliant, older horse for his young daughter. He offered to let me take my pick of the wild horses he had corralled there. Of course, I'd have to break the horse I picked.

I'd helped my dad break horses, but I'd never really broken one myself. Still, I didn't see it as the hardest job in the world. I picked a big brown colt, and the rancher put it into a smaller corral.

Leaving the big corral didn't sit well with the colt. He was pretty fired up when I got close to him, and roping him was a real job. After a while he calmed down a little, but the day I could actually ride him seemed a long way off.

The rancher didn't mind. He had space for me, and I did a few chores to pay for my meals. In the meantime, watching me try to break the colt amused him and the ranch hands.

To their surprise, it took me only a little over a week to throw my saddle onto the colt. Two days later I was riding him. When we left, I waved good-bye to the rancher's daughter. She was on my old horse.

Out of Luck

Ty and I hooked up again in Texas. We'd both signed on for the same cattle drive and were waiting for the long, hard winter to end.

When it did end, we rode to the ranch and got some bad news. Most of the cattle were dead from the harsh winter weather. Their bodies were lying on the range. It was a sorry sight.

I never will forget the sight of all those dead cattle in the spring thaw. It permeates all my memories of that time, the way that smoke permeates a closed room.

For Ty and me, that disastrous winter of 1886-1887 meant we weren't going on a cattle drive anytime soon.

Our money was about to run out when Ty got wind of some work. A big rancher over in the Texas panhandle was buying up wild mustangs and paying a good price per head.

I already knew that mustangs are also called broncos. They are smaller than other horses, but smart and tough.

My dad once told me that mustangs came from Arabian horses long ago. I couldn't understand how Arabian horses got to North America. Dad explained that Spanish explorers brought them here. Some of the Arabians got loose, turned wild, and bred with other wild horses.

I had heard, too, that most of the Native Americans' ponies were mustangs. They weren't wild anymore, of course. The Native Americans had tamed and bred them

According to what we learned, the rancher in Texas was buying up the stray horses for Buffalo Bill Cody's Wild West Show. That made sense, since the mustangs would put on a good show.

So Ty and I headed for the Texas panhandle. Along the way we picked up a couple of other cowhands to ride with us. They, too, were out of work because of the disastrous winter.

A Change in Plans

We ran into a herd of forty or so mustangs on the open range near the big ranch. As luck had it, they were a gentle bunch, and we managed to drive them into a large corral on the ranch.

The ranch owner was delighted and paid right up.

With money in our pockets and a good home-cooked meal in our bellies, we got ready to set out after more strays.

The rancher had another idea. He wanted to hire us on to break the horses we'd caught. Ty and the others turned him down. They didn't like getting tossed off of horses. I thought I could stand it, so I stayed on at the ranch.

Of course, I'd broken my own horse, but that was it. I really didn't know if I was meant for the job, but I soon found out.

I loved it! When I told that to the other cowhands, they acted as if I were crazy. It was just a job to them, and a tough one at that.

To me, it was fun. I even enjoyed the hard knocks. I felt as if I'd been born to break horses.

The horses seemed to sense the way I felt. They gave me a fair share of hard tosses, but they also became compliant quickly. I didn't realize it at the time, but I was building a reputation for this kind of work.

Then one day Buffalo Bill Cody appeared at the corral in person. He'd come to see me break a horse, and I became mighty nervous about that.

Everyone had heard of Buffalo Bill. People told how he rode for the Pony Express when he was only fourteen. Then he was a scout for the Union Army during the Civil War. After the war, he got a job providing buffalo meat to feed the men building the Kansas Pacific Railroad.

People say he killed more than 4,000 buffalo in less than eighteen months. That's how he got his name. I heard there were even books written about Buffalo Bill Cody's adventures. He'd sure had an exciting life.

Now Buffalo Bill was traveling all over the United States and Europe with his Wild West Show. Sitting Bull, a famous Sioux chief, traveled with the show. Annie Oakley, the best shot in the West, performed with the show, too.

Nervous or not, I did my riding and took my thumps. Later, the rancher told me that Mr. Cody wanted to see me.

Mr. Cody told me about something new he was adding to his Wild West Show. It was called bronco busting, and he wanted me to have a starring role. Wow!

I couldn't refuse. I took the job and even managed to talk him into hiring Ty as a cowboy in the show.

Since then Ty and I have been all over the country. I even had my dad and mom take a train to Omaha, Nebraska, to see one of our shows.

They were both thrilled. My dad was especially thrilled to shake the hand of Buffalo Bill Cody.

Before Dad and Mom left on their train trip home, I took them out to dinner at a fine restaurant. Dad said that he always knew I was going to make something of myself. Mom said that I was beginning to look a lot like Dad.

As for me, I was just glad to see their craggy faces once more.